The Tree Man

Robert Mazibuko's story

edited by Joanne Bloch

photographs by Joanne Bloch

NEW READERS PROJECT

The Tree Man: Robert Mazibuko's story

First published 1996 by
New Readers Project,
Department of Adult and Community Education
University of Natal, Durban
P/Bag X10 Dalbridge, 4014

Copyright © New Readers Project

Cover photograph by Joanne Bloch
Illustrations by Clive Pillay
Cover design by Lesley Lewis of Inkspots
Design and desktop publication by Lesley Lewis of Inkspots
Printed by Kohler Carton and Print (Natal)

ISBN: 1-86840-173-4

Zulu Title: Indoda Yezihlahla: Indaba kaRobert Mazibuko
ISBN: 1 - 86840 - 174 - X

Thanks

Thanks to the following people who helped with the content of this book:

Raymond Auerbach and Noel Oettle of the Farmer Support Group, University of Natal, Pietermaritzburg;

John Aitchison of the Centre for Adult Education, University of Natal, Pietermaritzburg.

Thanks to the following people from Rennies Cargo Terminals Level 3 English Group who gave their valuable time evaluating this book:

Michelle Plant, Carol Rae, Excellent Mbele, Isaac Goge, Emmanuel Masondo, Clement Mbonambi, Vusumuzi Dlamini, Anthony Shange and Marcus Mhlongo.

Thanks to the following people from the Adult Basic Education Co-operative (AABEC) Advanced English Group who gave up their valuable time evaluating this book:

Bommie Naicker, Busisiwe Cele, Krishnie Perumal, Charity Mzotho and Rejoice Mhlongo.

Introduction

Robert Mazibuko died on 11 July 1994 at the age of 90. He loved the soil and the land deeply and taught himself everything he could about how to look after it. All his long life he tried his best to teach people about the soil and compost which he called black gold. He taught people how important it is to plant trees. That is why he was given the name, "The Tree Man".

His ideas were simple. He believed that everything in nature is part of the whole, and that it is only by caring for our earth that we can really look after ourselves. Even the poorest families can feed themselves by looking after the soil and growing their own food.

With his trench farming method you make the soil fertile with compost made from leaves, grass, old food from the kitchen and animal droppings. You do not use chemicals or fertilisers. This is called organic farming. These ideas are now known around the world, but when he first taught them they were not well-known in South Africa.

Robert Mazibuko travelled all over the world talking about his farming methods, and in the years before his death he won many awards for his work. In 1991 he won the Durban Environmental Week Award for his conservation work. In 1993 he won a Green Trust Award, and in December 1993 he won the Department of Environmental Affairs Conservation Award.

What follows is his story in his own words, which he told to Joanne Bloch shortly before his death.

Robert Mazibuko with his black gold

Robert Mazibuko's story

My family history

I was born in 1904 near Ladysmith, at a place called Spioenkop. We lived on a big farm owned by a white man. My father looked after the farm during the Gold Rush while the owner was in Johannesburg. We had to help our father, so we learned how to keep cattle, shear sheep, milk cows, groom horses, cut hay, plough fields and care for crops.

My parents were not educated, but they could speak English and Afrikaans. They also knew how to do many useful things with their hands. They could grow food, keep animals and build huts.

There was a lot of craftwork in those days, because we had none of these gadgets which we use today. So the people used clay to make pots, and reeds and grasses for sleeping mats, beer strainers and water containers. They used wood to make pillows and milking pails.

In those days the children worked with their mothers in the fields. Each child also had a little garden. At that time, agriculture, the soil and animals were so important to the African people. They were our banks and mines. We lived because there were animals, pastures and water.

My parents were Christians and they obeyed the laws and the Commandments which the missionaries taught them. We had to be obedient. Our parents did not spare the rod to spoil the child. If you did anything naughty, especially to older people, they had to punish you. You could not complain.

It was also the tribal custom that every parent was the parent of every child, so if any man found you doing something wrong away from home, it was his duty to punish you. This tribal system taught us to respect each other. When I went to college, I felt respect for the principal, teachers and monitors because I had learnt this at home.

The white people we lived with in those days enjoyed our respect and respected us in turn. I can remember very well how the boss would slaughter a sheep and give half to my father and take half home. That working together, that feeling of brotherhood and sisterhood and sharing, was very common. Sometimes they would say, "Plough this field. I will give you the seed but we will divide. We'll share the products from the field."

In those days, it was custom to share with the community. Someone who had a lot of cattle would take boys from the poorer homes to take care of them. At the end of the year, each child was given a heifer. Sometimes those boys would do this until they were sixteen years old, so you can imagine how many cattle they had.

Say a man had a big field of mealies. When he was reaping, he would invite all the neighbours to come and help him. He would not pay them. He would only give them *mahewu*. If a rich man slaughtered an ox in winter time, he would make sure that the poorer members of the community got a share of that ox, without having to pay a penny. This spirit of sharing was a big influence on me.

My education

We were eight brothers. I was the fourth son, and the only one who wanted to forge ahead with my education. The others only went as far as Std 4, and then went off to work in Johannesburg to make money to pay their taxes. In those days there were so many taxes! We had to pay taxes on dogs, huts, weapons and also a poll tax. Also, you had to look smart and clothes were expensive. I had to work hard to earn money to buy my clothes.

Round about 1910 — the time of Halley's Comet — Methodist evangelists started a private school in my father's kraal, and employed a teacher to teach us our ABC. But soon my parents heard of a place called Driefontein, which had been bought by African people. They had built schools there to give African people a higher education. So my parents moved from Spioenkop to Driefontein. While our family stayed there, my father went to work on a dairy farm in Johannesburg.

When I started school at Driefontein in 1915, I found that the children had to do gardening as part of the syllabus. I had learned to love the soil when I was very young, both at home and in school at Spioenkop. So now I excelled. I remember that our headmaster and the school inspectors who came from Pietermaritzburg always admired my patch of garden. I passed my school-leaving certificate at Driefontein. This was the highest you could go in any school in Natal. I then went to St Francis Teachers' Training College at Mariannhill in 1928.

I studied under the Reverend Father Bernard Huss, a lecturer in agriculture. I am grateful that I met him as he taught me so much. He believed that the whole person must be educated — not only our brains but also our bodies. So at this school they taught us to fix chairs, blackboards and window panes. They taught us to help the community by building toilets and planting trees and vegetable gardens.

Reverend Huss also introduced me to organic gardening, which we did at home without even knowing the name "organic". But his way was much more organised, and I began to get very interested. Reverend Huss did not believe in using chemicals and fertilisers to make vegetables and plants grow. He taught us that they are too expensive, and they hurt the environment. Rather, he believed in using compost made from organic matter like reeds, grass and kitchen waste.

At two o'clock, all the trainee teachers went to their gardens. Each student had a garden to show how he would work when he was a qualified teacher. Farming, gardening and tree-planting were in my blood from when I was young. I said to myself it was just a gift from the heavens. Sister Glenantia, my teacher in 2nd year at college, soon noticed this, and put me in charge of all the flower gardens of St Francis College. Every morning and every afternoon I weeded and watered them.

This close connection with nature made me fall in love with it even more. I saw how insects like flowers, and how bees come and collect nectar and pollen, and how birds come and drink nectar from some of the bigger flowers.

Robert Mazibuko, a co-worker and a visitor at KwaDlamahlahla

My working life

After I finished college in 1930, I went to teach at many different schools. At every school I planted a few trees, started a vegetable garden and planted a hedge to stop dust from blowing into the school. At every school I built toilets for the school and then for the community. At first this was strange for most of the African people, but soon they realised how important toilets are to stop flies from breeding and spreading diseases.

In the early 1940s I worked as the principal of Hlophenkulu High School in Nongoma. I taught all the boys and girls to plant their own crops on the Mission lands. We planted lots of fruit trees and vegetables and the community was very pleased. Then we asked them to come and show the children how to make sleeping mats and beer strainers, and how to make sour milk in calabashes.

Sometimes I went with the superintendent of Hlophenkulu Mission Station, Reverend Robinson, on his travels. Sometimes we went right to the border of Portuguese East Africa. He would preach for 30 minutes, and then give me one hour to teach the African people that the soil is God, and that if they loved the soil and nature, then they would love the Holy Spirit too.

After I left Hlophenkulu I spent a year at Fort Cox Agricultural College in King William's Town, where I studied conventional agriculture. I learnt all about poisons and fertilisers and I began to understand the difference between conventional agriculture and organic farming. In the end, I decided the Reverend Huss was right. Poisons and fertilisers were not for me. Although they make plants grow very fast, they also die very fast. Also chemicals cannot work without much rain and moisture, so if it doesn't rain, they don't work. Another bad thing is that chemicals kill all the insects in the soil, even the good ones like earthworms.

I taught at many more schools in South Africa, as well as in Lesotho, Swaziland and Botswana. I also travelled all over Africa and the world, seeing how people lived and how they used the soil. I met many interesting people who were working in the field of organic farming and I learnt a lot from them. I found that I was not alone in believing that commercial agriculture and the use of chemicals have destroyed the soil. We need to plant more trees everywhere because their roots will go down and bring the water from down below up to the surface. Birds and animals will come back to live in the trees and their droppings, skins and nests will make the soil rich again. We also need to enrich the soil with compost, and practise organic farming. During all these years I was busy developing the system of trench farming.

In 1956 I went to work at the Valley Trust near Durban. By this time my method of organic farming, the trench system, worked perfectly. For 17 years I showed the people of the Valley of a Thousand Hills how to do organic farming. In all those years my crops did not fail once. This convinced me that when you feed the soil, the soil will feed the plants, and the plants will feed the people and the animals. God created all these things to work together!

In 1973, I went to work at the Edendale Lay Ecumenical Centre. For nearly 60 years I had thought about starting a school. I wanted to teach the youth how to use the soil to feed every mouth in every home. At last, in 1980, with the help of overseas funders, I was able to start the Africa Tree Centre, KwaDlamahlahla. Here I train boys and girls in the art and craft of vegetable growing, tree growing and environmental education.

Please go and see for yourself!

Robert Mazibuko at the entrance to KwaDlamahlahla

Lessons from the past

We need to learn some lessons from our ancestors. They were part of the land and at one with it. We need to look after our environment and use it as well as they did.

The African people knew so much about conservation because they moved around with their cattle. In this way, they learned which grasses, plants, trees and animals were useful, and where to find clean water.

Today we don't move about from place to place as our ancestors did. More people are born every day, and our cities are growing and growing. Millions of trees have been cut down, which has hurt our earth. Big farms where they grow crops like sugar cane for money have made the soil terribly weak. It has become too loose. When there is wind, soil is blown left and right, and its richness and goodness is blown away. Also when it rains heavily, the rich soil is washed into the rivers. It is now more important than ever to look after our earth.

In African culture, the people always respected the land, the trees, the plants, the animals, birds and insects. For example, there were many different birds that no-one was allowed to kill — like owls, *nkombose*, *ngete*, eagles, vultures, storks and tickbirds. These birds were too useful to kill. You could not kill a secretary-bird either. It was important because it killed snakes.

No-one could kill an elephant or a hippopotamus for any reason at all. Ant-bears were very important because they ate white ants, which destroy trees and homes. So nobody killed them. Some animals, like buck, could only be killed to make useful things out of their skins, like karosses and little slings for mothers to carry their babies in.

In the old days, certain trees were very important too. Most people were not allowed to touch the *inkayi* tree. Its wood was very hardy, so only warriors could break its branches to make fighting sticks. Many other trees and plants were important as herbal medicine was made from them. For example, no-one was allowed to destroy the tree called *mhlehampethu*, because it was used to treat sores on animals. No fly would come near an animal once its sores were covered with this *muthi*.

Our ancestors also knew the importance of clean water. There was a place called Ntonjaneni in KwaZulu. It was a spring, where the king and his family and followers drank water. Warriors used to guard this drinking well night and day so that no animal or person could dirty the water.

Water that the people used at home for drinking and washing in was covered with thorn bushes to keep the animals out. Sometimes they would build a little wall with stones. Then they would dig a pool below this place, so that the cattle could drink there.

In the old days, African people ate from the hand of nature. This made them very healthy and strong. The women and girls used to go out into the veld and collect wild spinach and fruits for their families to eat. They knew exactly how to keep seeds so that they would not be eaten by weevils and other insects. They hung the seeds near the top of the roof of the house, so that the smoke and soot made them go black. Then not even rats would eat them. These seeds grew very well because that soot was like fertiliser. Parents gave roasted pumpkin pips to their children to eat, because they knew that these pips kill worms like tapeworm and roundworm.

In summer-time, the women used to dry vegetables in the sun and store them inside at night. They would do this for many days. Then, in the winter-time when there were few vegetables, the dried vegetables would be as fresh as when they were picked.

To store mealies, they would dig a big hole, and line it with mealie stalks. Then they would put fresh mealie cobs inside. They would cover them with grass, cover that with soil and leave it for three months. In winter they would cook these mealies and they tasted fresh. Sometimes they would boil the mealies in salt and then hang them out in the sun to dry. When the men came home from hunting, or the children returned from the schools or colleges for holidays, there would be delicious food to eat.

There is a lot to learn from these stories of the past. Our ancestors understood that in nature everything is linked up or interconnected. The animals, insects and birds need the trees and plants. The trees and plants need the animals, insects and birds. People need all of them.

When last did you see an owl? These days owls are very rare, because there are so few grasses left in the veld. Without these grasses, there is no place for the rats to live in the veld. Without the rats, the owls have no food, so they die.

Many other South African wild animals like ant-bears and secretary-birds are rare now. When I was young I remember there were flocks of birds flying in the sky, eating insects like locusts and moths. Today it is very rare to see those birds. Yet if we looked after our environment, these birds would come back in their hundreds and so would the other rare animals.

What can we do now?

The very first thing to do to improve our environment is to plant trees. They should be indigenous trees — trees that come from South Africa and grow well here. They should also be trees that have fruit that is eaten by birds, animals and people. When there are many of these trees, monkeys and owls and other birds will come to live in them. Their droppings, and their bodies when they die, will make the soil rich again.

A donga or gulley in the veld is a sign that there is a problem in that place. All the soil is washing away when it rains. If we find a donga, we must try to grow some trees there. The trees' roots will hold the soil in place. The best seeds to plant are acacia seeds, because these trees are so strong.

It is interesting that in places where it is very dry, cattle will eat acacia leaves and thorns. This gives their meat a wonderful flavour. If you roast this meat on an open fire, you can see a blue flame on it, as though you had poured paraffin in the fire.

Meat you buy from a butchery tastes like rubber compared to this delicious meat!

It is also a very good idea to protect any wet places we find near our homes. We can plant aloes or trees like willows, so that animals do not tramp about there and dirty the water. Wetlands are like sponges which must not be broken or crushed. If you care for them by planting indigenous trees there, this means that there will be more water. This water will be fresh and clean, so people will not get sick from drinking it. Also, the land around the wet place is more fertile if there is more water.

We also need to plant trees next to the roads and highways. Many thousands of trees were cut down in the past to build these roads. They were never replaced so the soil has become poorer.

We can also plant different grasses, like *incema* which is good for making *ucansi* (sleeping mats), and the grass which we make brooms out of.

Without the soil, there is nothing

Conservation is vitally important for the future of our country. If we plant trees and grasses and look after our wetlands and wild birds and animals, we will be doing a lot. But there is something even more important we need to know. How do we practise conservation in our own gardens? How can we use our own little piece of land to help ourselves and help our earth too? We have to learn how to enrich our soil, because without the soil, there is nothing.

Everything that birds, animals and people eat comes from the soil. The plants and trees grow in the soil. From them we get wood, building materials and the raw materials from which many medicines are made. Gold, diamonds, precious stones and iron come from the soil. Without the soil there would be no fresh air, no water, no life at all. For me, the soil is our God.

So how do you look after this precious soil and enrich it so that it can keep on feeding and supporting us? The answer is that you must put back into the soil what you take out of it because nothing is useless to the soil. It feeds on all our rubbish. That's why the first thing to do in your garden is to start a compost heap — to make what I call black gold. Black gold is compost — made from old leaves, peels and sweepings from the kitchen, mixed with grass and animal manure. Once this breaks down, it is dark in colour, and I call it black gold because it will last much longer than any chemicals. Chemicals make plants grow very fast, but black gold gives plants the chance to grow naturally, taking many elements from the soil which are good for human bodies.

There are many plants out in the veld which have deep roots and which put goodness into the soil. These are the plants and trees I help people to find and grow because they make the soil healthier. People can also grow the vegetables that grew long ago, like wild tomato which will grow anywhere. Birds eat it and, because they cannot digest its seed, wherever the birds make droppings more plants grow.

Trench farming

Trench farming is a wonderful way of making the soil more fertile in a vegetable garden. You can use this method in a place where the soil is totally dead, even where ordinary plants like *maphusini* and *inkonkonye* cannot grow. You find such soil where there are many animals and people living in a small space. Trench farming is also a good way to grow vegetables and plants in places where there is little water.

Trench farming is when you dig a hole and fill it with organic matter and soil. This way of farming works very well because it copies a valley in nature. Valleys are always green, even in winter or in a dry season. This is because when it rains, all the organic matter from the mountains washes down into the valley. There the organic matter helps the soil to hold water. So these trenches are nothing else but little valleys which can give people something to eat.

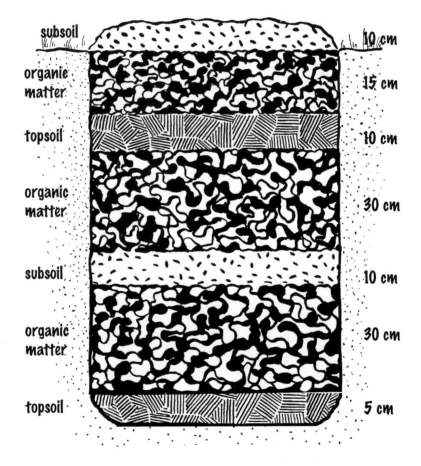

subsoil		10 cm
organic matter		15 cm
topsoil		10 cm
organic matter		30 cm
subsoil		10 cm
organic matter		30 cm
topsoil		5 cm

1. Dig a trench 1 metre deep, 1 metre wide and 6 metres long. (A metre is about as long as a broom handle.)

    Put the topsoil on one side of the trench. The topsoil is the soil which you dig out first from the top of the ground. It is a dark colour.

    Put the subsoil (the soil which is below the topsoil) in a pile on the other side of the trench. It is a reddish colour. Do not mix the topsoil with the subsoil.

2. Put a layer of topsoil at the bottom. It must be about 5cm deep. (5cm is about as long as a little finger.) This will put bacteria into the trench which will help in breaking down organic matter.

3. Collect a pile of grass, leaves, branches, animal droppings and old vegetables. This is called organic matter.

    Put this organic matter in the bottom of the trench. This layer should be about 30cm deep. (This is about the height of a metal bucket.)

Sprinkle the organic matter with a bucketful of water.

This will help it to rot quickly.

4. Now put in some subsoil. (This is the reddish soil that you dug out.)

   This layer should be about 10cm deep. (It should be about twice as deep as the first layer of topsoil.)

5. Put in another layer of organic matter 30cm deep. (This is the same amount of organic matter as before.)

   Sprinkle it with a bucketful of water.

6. On top of that put 10cm of topsoil.

7. Put in enough organic matter to fill the trench up to ground level.

8. Add 10cm of subsoil. This has got many minerals in it.

A large trench filled with organic matter

9.   Pour 300 to 500 litres (60 to 100 bucketfuls) of water onto the trench every 10 days.

10. After 5 or 6 weeks the trench will be ready for planting.

Planting

The first crop you plant must be a legume crop — beans or peas as they will add nitrogen to the soil. This is very important for growing other kinds of vegetables. It also helps the organic matter in the soil to rot.

Remember to rotate your plants. This means that you must not always plant the same kind of vegetable in the same place all the time. Start with a legume like peas. After harvesting, plant a leaf crop like cabbage. Then plant a root crop like carrots.

After ten or fifteen harvests you may have to dig the trench again and put in new organic matter.

Conclusion

History will remember Robert Mazibuko as one of the first South Africans who taught others about conservation and organic farming. He inspired thousands of people to make the soil better for growing food. He deeply loved, respected and understood the soil, the trees and people.

He always said, "You must find my people where they are."

Robert Mazibuko wanted the Africa Tree Centre to be owned and run by the people. He brought together many community leaders and people who know about nature and conservation to run the Africa Tree Centre.

Robert Mazibuko planted a seed which has started to grow. Many people must now join hands to help the seed to grow into a strong and fruitful tree.